THE WORLD OF ANDY CAPP

As seen every day in the Daily Mirror

TCH! JUST LOOK AT HIM —

GET IN HERE — I'LL TEACH YOU TO KEEP ME UP TILL THIS TIME OF NIGHT—!

ARE YOU COMING IN OR AREN'T YOU?!

Z 97

MARRIAGE CAN TEACH A MAN JUST ABOUT EVERYTHING EXCEPT HOW TO *BE* ONE

HAIRDRESSING SALON

YOU LOOK GREAT, FLO

YOU DO, TOO, PET—

THANKS

BUT AT OUR AGE, WHAT GOOD DOES IT DO US?

Z 98

OH, NO! I LEFT MY HANDBAG IN THE PUB, RUBE —!

DON'T WORRY, FLO —THE BARMAID'S AN HONEST LASS—

SHE'LL HAND IT OVER TO ANDY—

Z 99

EEEK

STAFF
ENTRANCE

NOTICE THAT? NOT A WORD OF THANKS FOR HOLDING THE FORT ALL DAY TILL SHE GETS BACK

Z109

WHAT'S THE PROBLEM? ARE YOU TAKING ME BACK OR *NOT?*

ER, COULD YOU COME BACK LATER-?

Z110

IN OUR SITUATION, IT TAKES A LOT OF CAREFUL THINKING JUST TO BE UNDECIDED - RIGHT?

ESPECIALLY WHEN SHE'S WATCHING A TV FILM AT THE SAME TIME

IF YOU ENJOY YOUR WORK, YOU CARRY ON, ADA-

Z111

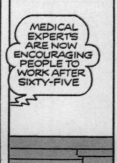

MEDICAL EXPERTS ARE NOW ENCOURAGING PEOPLE TO WORK AFTER SIXTY-FIVE

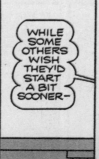

WHILE SOME OTHERS WISH THEY'D START A BIT SOONER-

HOW ABOUT SOME SERVICE AROUND HERE?!!

Panel 1: Y'KNOW, PET, THERE'S NOT A DAY GOES BY WITHOUT ME THINKING WHAT A WONDERFUL WIFE I'VE GOT—

Z124

Panel 2: ALL RIGHT, ALL RIGHT—!

Panel 4: WOULD YOU MIND MAKING IT EVERY OTHER DAY?

Panel 5: OFF!

Panel 6: JUST A MINUTE, PERCY—!

Panel 7: NATTER NATTER NATTER NATTER

Z125

Panel 8: IT'S OKAY, PET— IT HAD ABSOLUTELY NOTHING TO DO WITH THE RENT ARREARS WE OWE HIM

Panel 9: WHAT'S YOUR NEW LODGER LIKE, MUM?

CULTURED, FLO

Z126

Panel 10: IN WHAT WAY, MUM?

WEL-LL, YOU KNOW, FLO—

Panel 11: YES, WE KNOW—CULTURED IS ROUGHLY THE WAY THAT ANY OTHER BLOKE CARRIES ON, AND I DON'T!

2136

2137

2138

THE *TIME!* WHAT AM I GOING TO SAY? WHAT AM I GOING TO SAY—?

TCH! USE YOUR HEAD, MAN... ...LISTEN—

—OH, GREAT! THANKS, ANDY, *THANKS!*

I CAN'T STAND 'EM —THESE BLOKES WHO GET INTO TROUBLE BUT HAVEN'T THE FOGGIEST ABOUT HOW TO GET OUT OF IT

Z151

DO YOU KNOW HIM?

WHO?

THE BLOKE WHO WRITES THE MATCH REPORTS IN THE LOCAL PAPER

WHY? WHAT DOES HE HAVE TO SAY ABOUT MY PLAY?

NOT A WORD —*MUST* BE A FRIEND OF YOURS

LOOK, IF YOU CAN'T AFFORD TO GO TO BINGO, DON'T TAKE IT OUT ON *ME!*

Z152

STAFF ENTRANCE

BOSS OR NO BOSS, HE HAD NO RIGHT TO SPEAK TO ME LIKE THAT, FLO—

I'M DEFINITELY GOING TO HAND IN MY NOTICE TOMORROW!

YOU TAKE EVERYTHING SO SERIOUSLY, RUBE. IS IT WORTH IT—?

ANDY ALWAYS MAINTAINS THAT LIFE IS JUST A DREAM...

BUT JUST DARE TO WAKE HIM UP TO ASK WHY HE HASN'T GOT THE TEA READY

Z156

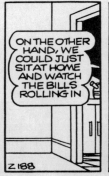

Z250

FLO, THAT LASS AT THE END OF THE BAR—

WASN'T SHE THE IMAGE OF THE BARMAID WHO USED TO BE AT THE STAR AND GARTER—?

I COULDN'T SAY

CAN'T YOU RECALL —THE BLONDE—?

NO, I DISTINCTLY REMEMBER FORGETTING HER

FISH CHIPS

Z251

LOOK, CHALKIE, I HAPPEN TO BE YOUR BEST FRIEND—

AND I HAPPEN TO BE THE REFEREE —OFF!

YOU JUST NEVER LEARN

HOW CAN I LEARN WHEN PEOPLE HAVE A PERSONALITY CHANGE AND FORGET TO TELL ME ABOUT IT?!

Z252

GOOD EVENING —NICE TO HAVE YOU DROP IN, MUM-IN-LAW—

LOOK ME IN THE FACE AND DENY THAT YOU'RE ONLY SAYING THAT BECAUSE YOU WANT TO TAKE SOME MONEY OFF ME AT DOMINOES

YES, IT MUST BE BECAUSE I WANT TO TAKE SOME MONEY OFF YOU AT DOMINOES

☆@☆ ◎*☆*—!

BANG GOES ANOTHER —LITTLE HOMILY —'THE WAY TO WIN FRIENDS IS TO LET 'EM WIN ARGUMENTS'

'BYE, MOTHER, WE'LL LOOK IN AGAIN THIS EVENING

Z253

I'M WORRIED ABOUT HER, PET

A SICKROOM FULL OF FLOWERS AND YOU'RE WORRIED ABOUT HER—

I KNOW IT'S SILLY, BUT—

LOOK, SHE'LL RECOVER — FOLKS ROUND HERE AREN'T GIVEN TO SENDING FLOWERS TWICE

THAT'S A THOUGHT

Smythe

SHE'S A BIT YOUNGISH FOR MY OLD LINE OF PATTER, JACK, BUT HERE GOES—

THEY'RE NOT MUCH DIFFERENT TO THE OLDER ONES, ANDY...

AND THE SAME TO YOU!!

THEY MIGHT BE A BIT BETTER EDUCATED THESE DAYS, BUT THE LANGUAGE IS MUCH THE SAME

Z254

Smythe

THE ARGUMENTS ME AND ERIC HAVE, HE'S DRIVING ME NUTS. I JUST CAN'T GET THROUGH TO HIM—

SIMPLE SOLUTION, GIVE HIM THE PUSH

A WOMAN WILL STICK TO A MAN NO MATTER *HOW* STUPID HE MAY BE—

Smythe

Z255

ASK YOUR MISSUS!

OH, DEAR, DEAR. A BIT TOUCHY, ARE WE?

STAFF ENTRANCE

THEY FINALLY GAVE ME THAT BONUS, PET

ABOUT TIME! NOW DON'T GO THROWING IT AWAY ON BINGO — PUT IT AWAY AND PRETEND YOU DIDN'T GET IT—

Z292

NOT A BAD IDEA —IF YOU HADN'T BEEN PRETENDING I'D ALREADY HAD IT!!

SEND HIM OFF VICAR! IT'S A SIN THE WAY HE TACKLES!

HE'S RIGHT, ANDY, AND YOU CAN GUESS MY ATTITUDE TOWARDS SINS!

Z293

SAME AS MINE, VICAR — THEY CAN'T BE UNDONE, ONLY FORGIVEN, EH?

THANKS FOR FEEDING HIM WHILE I WAS AWAY, MUM—

THAT'S OKAY, FLO

I THINK IT WAS REAL BIG OF YOU, KNOWING WHAT YOU THINK OF HIM

MY PLEASURE, DEAR

Z294

GET YOUR PURSE OUT

SHE ACTS LIKE A SAMARITAN, CHARGES LIKE A PLUMBER

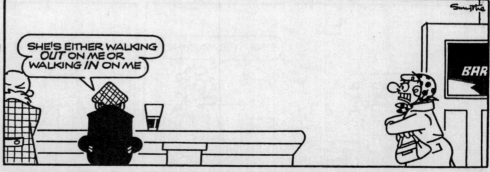

I CAN ALWAYS COME UP WITH SOMETHING IF I PUT MY MIND TO IT —

RUBE! GUESS WHAT I'VE DECIDED TO WEAR AT THAT WEDDING NEXT WEEK—

FLO! BEFORE YOU GET OFF TO WORK, COULD YOU—

NO, I COULDN'T! I DON'T SEE WHY I SHOULD FLOG MYSELF TO DEATH JUST TO KEEP YOU IN BEER MONEY!

A20

WELL, SOMEBODY HAS TO—!

THERE'S A LOT OF IT ABOUT

HERE'S ME OUT ENJOYING MESELF, AND THERE'S FLO WAITING UP FOR ME...

A LOVELY LASS LIKE THAT... WHAT SORT OF A BLOKE AM I-?

...TCH, I WISH I HAD A BETTER NATURE I COULD APPEAL TO...

A22

I THOUGHT YOU WERE PAINTING THAT FRONT DOOR—

I AM — I'M DOING IT DURING THE COMMERCIALS

A23

I'VE DECIDED TO GIVE IT ANOTHER GO, RUBE. DO ME A FAVOUR AND BREAK THE ICE, EH?

TCH! TCH! IF YOU INSIST—

ARE YOU AWAKE? FLO'S OUTSIDE—

WHAT'S SHE DOING HERE?

SHE'S HERE BECAUSE SHE'S NOT ALL THERE!

A24

SHE'S ALWAYS ON AT ME, ANDY. I WONDER IF LEAVING HER FOR A WHILE MIGHT BRING HER TO HER SENSES... WHAT DO YOU THINK?

A MATTER OF TIMING, WALTER

—JUST LONG ENOUGH FOR HER TO MISS YOU, BUT NOT LONG ENOUGH FOR HER TO WONDER WHY SHE EVER GOT STUCK WITH YOU IN THE FIRST PLACE

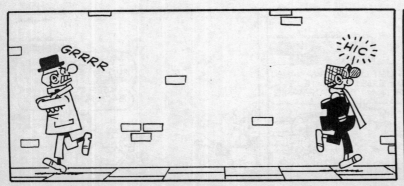

IS HE READY FOR OUR WEEKLY CHAT, FLO?

COME IN, VICAR. I'LL SEE WHAT I CAN DO —

HE'LL HAVE A JOB GETTING *THIS* BLOKE INTO HEAVEN — IT'S HARD ENOUGH JUST GETTING HIM OUT OF BED

A31

WHAT'S THE MATTER, TOM?

I'M FED UP. I'M SICK OF BEING AT THE BOTTOM OF THE PILE

OH, IS *THAT* ALL — DON'T WORRY ABOUT IT, MATE

LOOK, WHEN YOU ARE STANDING IN A BUS SHELTER AND IT'S RAINING AND BLOWING A GALE, DON'T YOU WISH YOU HAD A CAR?

NO, NOT REALLY — I USUALLY WISH I HAD THE BUS FARE

AMBITIOUS HE *AIN'T*

A32

I'VE NEVER SEEN YOU LOOK SO WORRIED, FLO

YOU NOTICED?

EVERYONE HAS. YOU HAD A WORRIED LOOK ON YOUR FACE ALL DAY LONG AT WORK —

PITY YOU'RE NOT LIKE ANDY

NOBODY'S LIKE *HIM*

HE SAVES ALL HIS WORRIES FOR A SPECIFIC PART OF THE DAY — THEN TAKES A NAP THROUGH IT

Z

A33

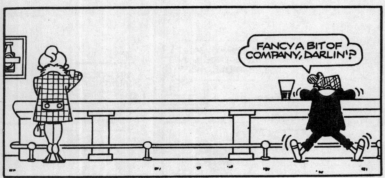

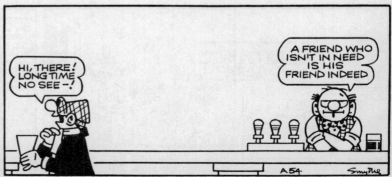

ANDY'S GAME SEEMS TO HAVE IMPROVED THIS SEASON, FLO

HE TRIES TO LEARN FROM THE MISTAKES OF OTHERS, RUBE

IT'S ONE OF THE BEST WAYS, FLO

IT'S THE *ONLY* WAY, RUBE – HE'S NEVER ON THE FIELD LONG ENOUGH TO MAKE 'EM ALL HIMSELF

A64

ANYONE IN HERE OWN THAT PORSCHE PARKED ON THE CORNER?

BAR

WHAT COLOUR?

=HIC=

IGNORE HIM, ALAN – HE'S TRYING TO IMPRESS A NEW FACE

A65

HE'S LIKE YOUR MAN, FLO. THE AIMLESS TYPE, NO DIRECTION IN LIFE –

NOT *MY* MAN, MARTHA. HE KNOWS *EXACTLY* WHERE HE WANTS TO GO –

A66

AND COME OPENING TIME, HE'S OFF LIKE A SHOT

SHE HAS NO REFERENCES OR EXPERIENCE AS A BARMAID, ANDY, BUT WHAT DO YOU THINK?

SHE'S DEFINITELY FILLED OUT BETTER THAN HER APPLICATION FORM, JACK

DEFINITELY

A85

WHEN CAN YOU START, DEAR?

Smythe

I'VE JUST MOVED INTO THIS AREA, MISTER... I CAN PLAY A BIT OF FOOTBALL—

ANY CHANCE OF GETTING INTO YOUR TEAM?

SCORED ANY GOALS LATELY?

NO — BUT I'VE MADE DARN SURE THAT THE OTHER FLIPPIN' LOT HAVEN'T EITHER

A86

NAME—?

Smythe

NICE PAINT JOB ON THOSE WINDOW FRAMES, HARRY—I'VE GOT TO HAND IT TO YOU

I DIDN'T DO IT, MY MISSUS DID—

A87

LIKE I SAID—I'VE GOT TO HAND IT TO YOU

ALES

Smythe

WHAT A DAY I'VE HAD AT WORK, PET. HOW WAS YOUR DAY?

A97

DON'T MENTION IT — IT'S BEEN AS BAD AS YESTERDAY. I'M ABSOLUTELY WORN OUT

TCH, TCH! I'LL MAKE YOU A NICE CUP OF TEA, EH?

THERE'S NOTHING MORE EXHAUSTING THAN TOSSING AND TURNING ALL DAY LONG TRYING TO DROP OFF TO SLEEP

Smythe

TCH, I PLAYED LIKE A RIGHT CLOWN...

YOU WERE SUPPOSED TO BE AT THE INTERVIEW FOR THAT JOB I WROTE AFTER FOR YOU — YOU NEVER RESPECT MY WISHES —!!

A98

LOOK, MISSUS, THAT FLIPPIN' CUE OF MINE VERY RARELY RESPECTS MY WISHES, BUT I DON'T GO TO PIECES ABOUT IT

Smythe

ALL SET FOR THE BIG DAY, SANDRA, NO SECOND THOUGHTS?

JUST A WEENY BIT WORRIED — PEOPLE SAY BOB'S A BIT LIKE UNCLE ANDY IN SOME WAYS

A99

DON'T WORRY TOO MUCH ABOUT THAT, PET —

ONCE YOU FACE UP TO THE FACT THAT YOU CAN'T RELY ON HIM FOR ANYTHING, THE REST IS PLAIN SAILING

THANKS A LOT. I CAN HARDLY WAIT

FISH-CHIPS

Smythe

ARE YOU OKAY, PERCY?

I'LL LET YOU KNOW LATER

AFTER A TACKLE BY *THAT* LAD IT'S A QUESTION OF HOW MANY LAST GASPS YOU CAN GASP

A100

GOODNIGHT, DARLIN'

BAR

DON'T WORRY, SWEET'EART, SHE'S WELL DOWN THE LIST

WHO'S WORRIED?

SHE'LL NEVER MOVE UP TO NUMBER ONE – THERE'S TOO MANY PIGEONS IN THE WAY

A101

STAFF ENTRANCE

FANCY COMING OUT FOR A DRINK, PET?

WHAT?!!

YOU'VE GOT TO ASK 'EM AT THE RIGHT TIME

YOU WERE THE BEST PLAYER ON THE FIELD, ANDY. NOBODY CAN READ A GAME LIKE YOU—

THANKS, PERCY

A106

YOU NOTICE EVERYTHING THAT'S GOING ON AROUND YOU

HE EVEN NOTICED THAT I DIDN'T TURN UP TO WATCH HIM

GRRRR

DON'T YOU ORDER ME ABOUT! JUST WAIT YOUR TURN!

A107

HE'S GETTING ON VERY WELL WITH THAT NEW BARMAID, FLO

YOU'RE RIGHT RUBE, I'VE NOTICED THE WAY SHE TALKS TO HIM—

HEY! JUST HOW CLOSE ARE YOU TWO?!

I WARNED YOU YESTERDAY TO KEEP OUT OF MY HANDBAG UNLESS YOU'VE GOT MY PERMISSION—!!

A108

I ONLY EVER TAKE LITTLE AMOUNTS

HE'S RIGHT— LITTLE AMOUNTS ON A MASSIVE SCALE—!

Laugh with Andy Capp every day...

in Britain's brightest newspaper – The Daily Mirror